The Book

by
Gordy
Jones

Illustrated by
Tim VanNess

To Tommy, a genuine Baseball Guy.
G.J.

In Memory of Number 34,
Kirby Puckett

First Edition

Publication Data
Jones, Gordy.
Baseball Guy: The Book / by Gordy Jones ; illustrated by Tim VanNess ; layout by Paul Bergly Ink LLC ; audio compact disk narrated by Dave Lee ; audio engineering by Mike Lynch, Dave Anton and Paul Bergly

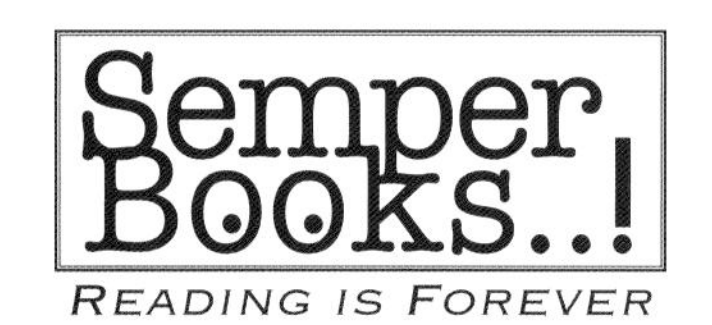

www.baseballguy.org

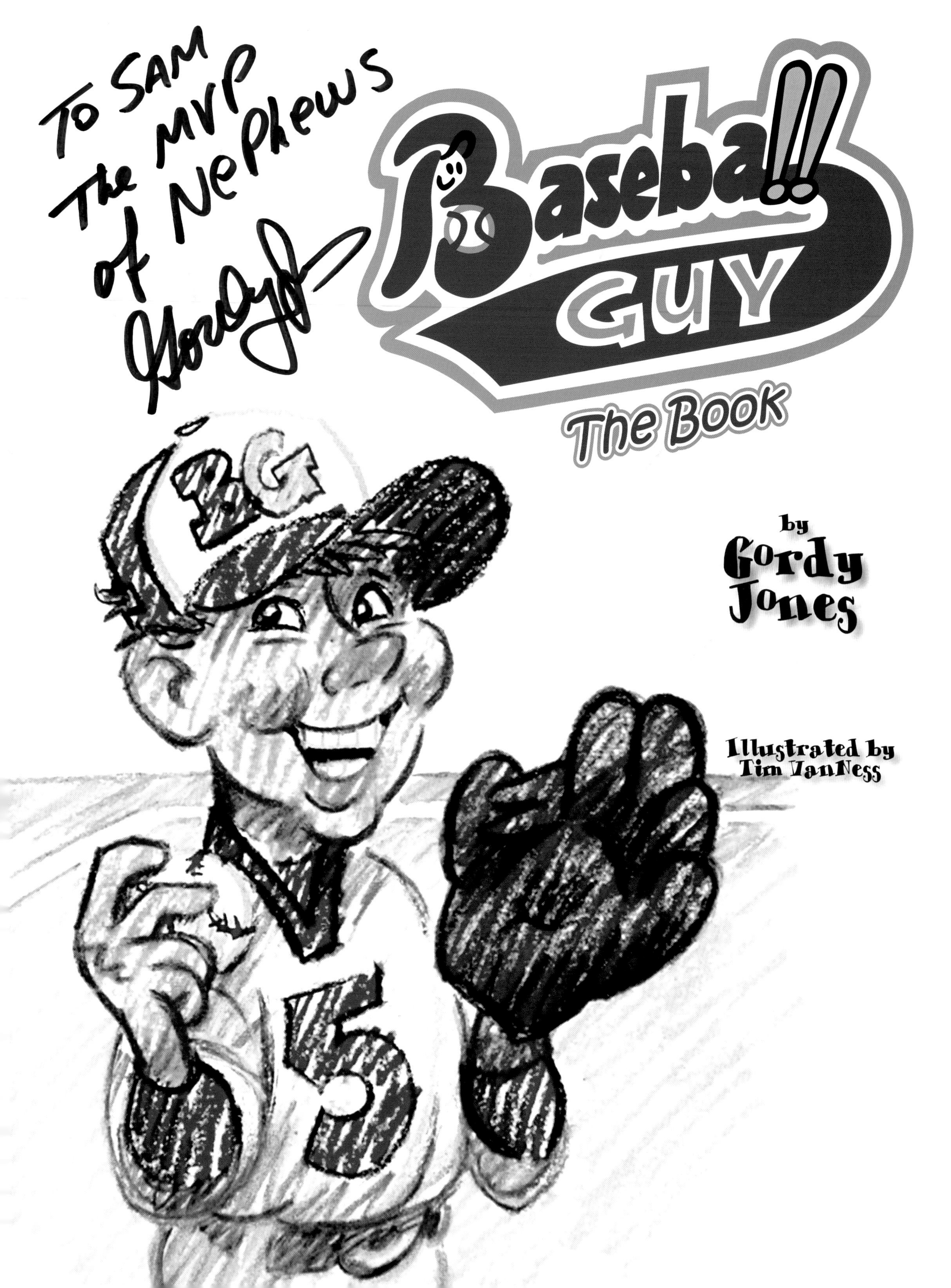
To SAM
The MVP
of Nephews
Baseball
GUY
The Book
by
Gordy
Jones
Illustrated by
Tim VanNess

I'm going to be a big baseball guy.
When I'm up to bat, the baseball will fly,
The white ball will soar, through the blue sky.

Up over the fence, and into the bleachers,
Where there sit many, big baseball creatures.
They run and they scramble, chasing the ball.
That's what they do, when it's hit over the wall.

But first I must practice every chance that I get,
Throwing and fielding, hey! It's my turn to hit!
Where can we practice? The old sandlot is gone.
The playground! The playground!
The playground at dawn!

First thing in the morning, to the playground we'll go.
There's Steve, Dave, and Lori, and our catcher Joe.

We will throw and we'll catch,
We'll catch and we'll throw.

We'll learn signals and signs.
There is so much to know.

We'll choose sides for a game when we get together.
But what if it rains? Let's hope for good weather!
We'll compete against others, once we form a team,
Little League is so fun, it's like eating ice cream.

We'll play very hard, but respect one another!
We all love to play baseball.
Look, here comes my mother!

She’s at most of my games, my mom is so nice.
She knows all the kid’s names!
She brings water and ice.

Yes, I'm going to be a big baseball guy.
I'm going to practice. I'll really try.

I'll try out for the team that they have at high school.
Oh Man! If I made it, that'd really be cool.
To play with chalked baselines,
And a chalked batter's box,
Full uniforms, too,
Right down to the socks.

The pitcher is tall and
He throws very fast.

He throws to the catcher.
Hey! He wears a mask.

The umpire is behind him,
His face is masked, too.

Look down at my feet.
I have cleats on my shoes.

The coach says we must practice, so let us begin.
That's what it takes, if you want to win.
I'll play baseball in college, and earn my degree,
I'll learn about business, writing, and photography.
I'll listen to the professor and to all of the teachers.
Then I'll go to the ballpark, and reach for the bleachers.

Then after college,
There would be nothing finer,
Than to sign with a team,
And play ball in the minors.

We'll play many games, so far away.
We'll take bumpy long bus rides, for most of the day.
I'll read a good book, as I ride on the bus.
I'll sit with my new friend, a fellow named Gus.

Together we'll play on freshly cut grass.
I'll field that fast grounder, I won't let it pass.

I'll have to throw hard,
The first baseman's in sight.
They light up the field,
For games played at night.

I'll train very hard to be one of the best.
I'll wear a cap and a shirt,
With my team's name on my chest.

Then one day, just maybe,
I'll get that big call.
I'll go up to the majors
Where I'll play ball
In brick baseball parks,
Historic and royal.
I'll smell food in the air,
For the fans that are loyal.

I'll fly on jet airplanes,
With other big leaguers…
Hotels big as castles…
I'll get paid to wear sneakers.

When I reach the majors
The coach will say,
"Be here early tomorrow.
We still practice each day."

We'll be first at the field.
When there's no one there yet.
When we lose a game,
Our fans get upset.

So we'll work every day
To sharpen our skills.
We'll dive for the ball,
We'll give the fans thrills.

My dedication will pay off,
I’ll have practiced so hard.
I’ll soon have my picture
On a Topp’s baseball card!

There'll be so much to do
When I achieve all this fame.
Children will stop me, "Sir! Please sign your name."
I'll visit children at schools, and at hospitals too.
And when I play baseball, it's bubblegum that I'll chew.

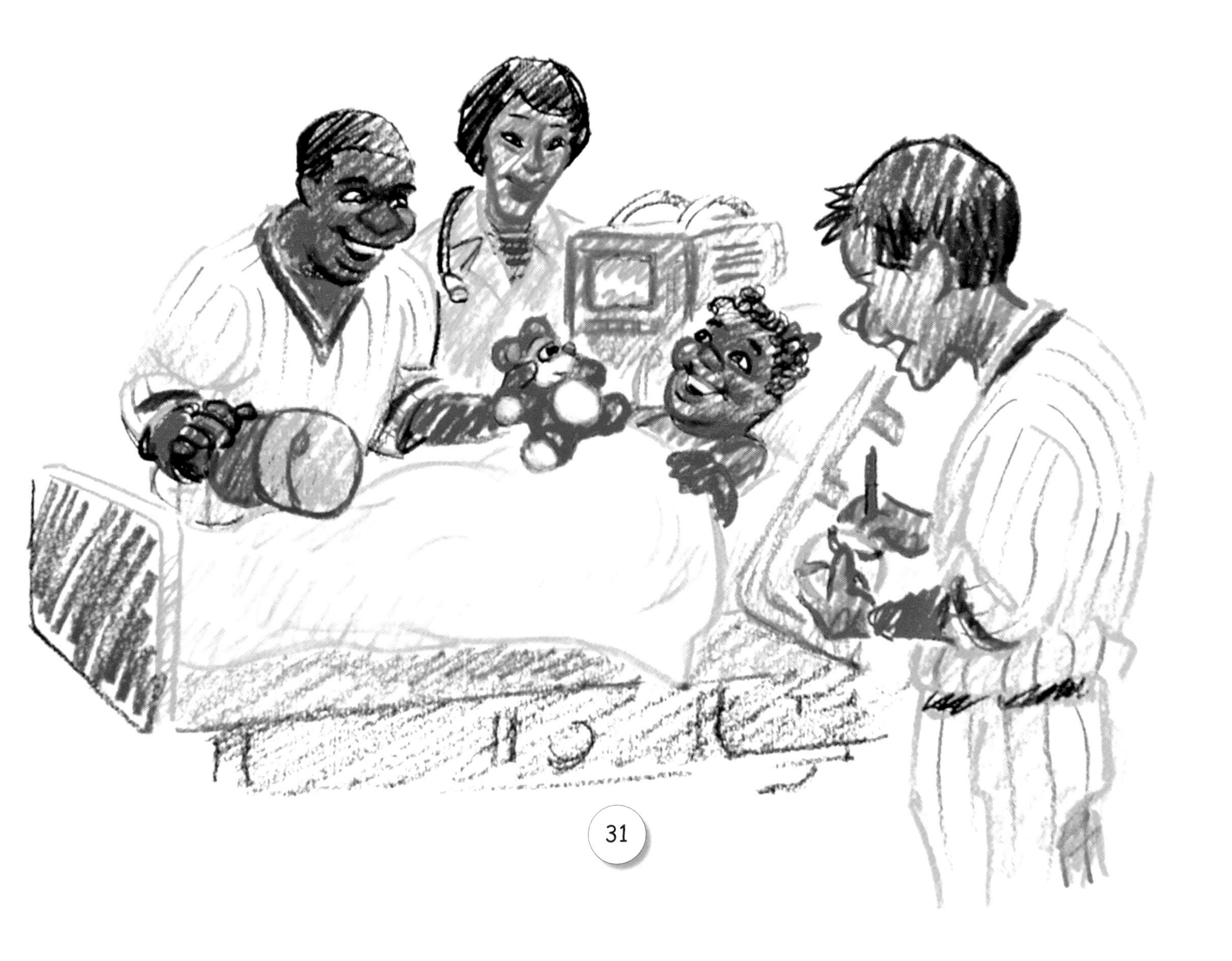

WHOA!
What's happening?
Where am I?
I'm in the stands screaming.
I'm not the batter!
I'm a fan that's just dreaming!

As a young boy
I really did try.
I wanted so badly
To be a big baseball guy.

Now I sit with my children and we watch from our seats.
I read over my program and we eat tasty treats.
The fans are a ***huge*** part of the game.
We cheer for our team and call the players by name.
So I guess you could say I'm a big baseball guy.
I yell to the batter, "Hey, Gus! Hit us a fly!"

Whether you're watching or playing,
You'll have loads of fun,
There are two outs in the 9th,
Go hit a home run!

AFTERWORD

Baseball Guy has nothing to do with gender; it is a state of mind. Millions enjoy this state of mind. It starts in childhood. You usually begin to feel it while playing catch with mom or dad and then with other kids at the field.

All fans are baseball guys! Some are in the stands, and some are watching and listening to the radio or TV. You couldn't play the game without the fans.

Going to a game is an event like nothing else. When you arrive at a ballpark you'll notice a happy carnival atmosphere surrounding the stadium. The ballpark has it's own unique, smells, sounds and sights. Baseball guys are everywhere and everyone is happy. You'll see a smiling ticket taker, followed by smiling ushers and the vendors who sing out names of baseball foods. They are all baseball guys. And everyone loves being at the park. The announcers, cameramen, photographers, reporters, the grounds crew, the front office, the coaches and the players; they are all important elements that make the baseball diamond sparkle. Not everyone can shine on the field. Some might rather work in another part of the game. That's why education is so important. Have fun playing ball and give it all you've got! But if you want to go in a different direction, there are many avenues you can take to be involved in this great game.

Kirby Puckett, Gordy Jones

Paul Molitor, Gordy Jones

Gordy Jones, Dave Winfield

You might even write a book!

I'd like to dedicate this book to everyone in baseball and thank them. Especially Dave St. Peter and the Minnesota Twins Family (this organization really is a family). Thanks to my dad; he taught me the game of baseball before I could walk. I remember those great days with him at the Met. He now watches from his box seat in heaven. He was a good man and quite the baseball statistician. Then I want to thank my little buddy Tommy Arnold. You inspired me as I wrote this book. You are a great friend. And I can't forget to thank his brother Danny Arnold. Thank You Steve Winfield, you are THE pillar of the community. And to his brother Dave Winfield, thanks for all that you have taught me. Thanks to Mike Jones who just graduated from the University of Minnesota — congratulations! Thank you, Sue Hayden, you are very special. Thanks Katie and Clint Arnold, Char and Carol Jones, Mario Casciano, Paul Bergly, Shooter, Mike Lynch, Dave Lee, and future slugger Tommy Jones. I couldn't have done it without you all.

PLAY BALL!

Gordy Jones

The love of baseball starts with youth and lasts a lifetime. Kids learn to play the game by having fun, and most of them don't even know the life lessons they are learning from participation in baseball. This book spells out some of those lessons.

People who've played baseball in the programs of the St. Paul, Minnesota, Parks and Recreation department were inspiration behind this book. The people and programs from this area continue to be models of excellence by offering and playing this great game of baseball.

To all — including you coaches and parents, continue to inspire our kids in this great sport. You'll be hitting a home run! —Dave Winfield, Inducted Member, National Baseball Hall of Fame Player

Dave Winfield, Steve Winfield, WCCO Radio Minnesota Twins broadcaster John Gordon

The story ***Baseball Guy*** brings back memories of growing up with my brother David. From the fun of playing baseball at the local playgrounds in St. Paul, to the dreams of playing pro ball one day, and to the pride in our mother's eyes watching her two boys play together.

From years of coaching and instructing both youth and parents, the one thing that I have come to realize; and that is for parents to be supportive... but make sure you let the kids have fun! ***Baseball Guy*** reflects a wonderful innocent time in our lives. Not just boys and girls growing up and having dreams, but believing in those dreams enough that sometimes... maybe someday... they just might even come true. Good luck! — Steve Winfield

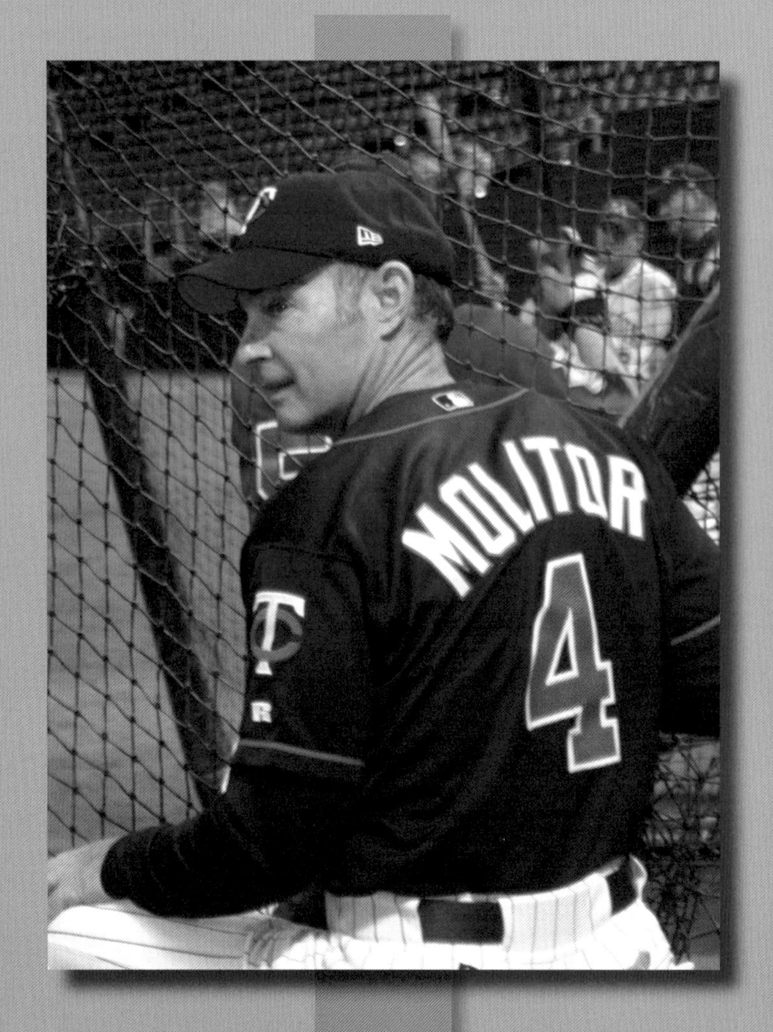

Gordy Jones's ***Baseball Guy*** is a great little story that speaks of a child's passion for baseball as well as his desire to learn the lessons of life:

- respect
- humility
- honesty
- perseverance
- and servanthood.

Well done!

—Paul Molitor,
Inducted Member,
National Baseball Hall of Fame

Gordy Jones put an emphasis on the importance of practicing and training regularly when he wrote *Baseball Guy*. Some people may think that practice is only important to children and amateur baseball players. Nothing could be further from the truth. In the majors, there's always another athlete ready to take your place if you fail. Professional ballplayers must always be at the top of their game.

I practice and train nearly everyday of the year. There are many days when I'm the first guy at the ballpark and the last one to leave. I find practice so important I continue to train through the off season, too.

When I was a seven-year-old kid growing up in Minnesota, winter made our baseball season way too short. My dad was trying to help me figure out a way to get swings in all year long. He mounted a curved PVC pipe on a post. It was high enough so I could drop a ball in one end, and have my bat up and ready to swing by the time it rolled out the other side. That was the invention of the QUICKSWING, which has come a long way since back then. QUICKSWING is now portable and adjustable. It is used in training by everyone from small children to major league baseball players and is endorsed by Baseball Hall of Fame's Paul Molitor.

Have fun and practice often.

—Joe Mauer, Minnesota Twins Player

For more information check out *www.quickswing.com*. —G.J.

I read my friend Gordy Jones's book ***Baseball Guy*** and was really impressed how he incorporated, not only the importance of hard work and practice, but also the importance of having a dream and the passion that goes along with chasing that dream.

I feel that ***Baseball Guy*** is not only a great read for kids who love baseball, but also a great read for the fan in all of us.

—Michael Cuddyer
Minnesota Twins Player

In the story ***Baseball Guy***, Gordy Jones mentions teamwork. I feel that teamwork is a very important part of the game. Nine individuals take the field, and each person has a job to do. We count on one another to get the job done. We seem to sense what the other's are thinking. Each person seems to know where the other eight players are going to be on any given play. Nine individuals come together to form one team, one unit. And teamwork comes from a lot of practice.

Jake, Corri, Lew and Jordan Ford

Team members spend a lot of time together. Major League players spend over eight months together training, playing and traveling. They can become very close friends, almost like a family.

Fans are very important to the game of baseball, too. When our fans cheer, it makes playing the game even more fun! We have great fans and I love meeting them. I know as long as I play my hardest, our fans will support us. They stand behind us in good times and in bad. Our fans are so important to me. I would never want to do anything off the field to disappoint them.

If I'm ever having a bad day or feeling a bit down, the fans always seem to lift my spirits!

I remember my first at bat in Minnesota. Everyone began howling: "Lew, Leeeeew!" I didn't know what they were saying, or what was going on. When I went back to the dugout one of the guys said that they had been booing me. I wondered why, what's going on? Later when I found out they were calling my name, "Lew" I thought it was really funny, and now I love it!

—Lew Ford, Minnesota Twins Player

When I was a youngster, all I wanted to do when I grew up was to be a sports columnist and a major league baseball player. I was able to do both, mainly because baseball — pitching for the Minnesota Twins in 1969 — provided me with the background and expertise to become a newspaper reporter. And, you never know when your baseball career will end, so it's important to have options you enjoy. —Charlie Walters
Sports Writer
Saint Paul Pioneer Press

Inspiration comes in many forms and for many of us, baseball was one of the first. Nothing can match that first glove that you had! What a special time it was when we rode our bikes to each other's houses in the summer and got enough kids — boys and girls — to play ball!

Gordy has captured that childhood magic with, *Baseball Guy*. The magic isn't just the look in your child's face when you read it with them, but the nostalgia and the memories that it generates in you as well. My vote for Rookie-of-the-Year is this initial effort by newspaper veteran, but first time author, Gordy Jones! —Dave Lee, WCCO Radio, Minneapolis

There isn't a child who plays catch with his or her father or mother who doesn't dream that someday they will become a "big leaguer." Yes, it's okay for that youngster to dream, but not every kid can make to the "big show." But just because that youngster doesn't have the ability to play baseball, it does not mean he or she can't become a "big leaguer" in some capacity. There are lots of opportunities. You can make it to the "big leagues" as a trainer, a writer, a scout, a traveling secretary, or as a broadcaster. I just happened to make it as a radio announcer for the Minnesota Twins.

While there are many former players who have made it to the broadcast booth (example: Dan Gladden, Jack Morris, Bert Blyleven) some broadcasters never played professional baseball but have been around enough to be able to "talk" a good game and portray the unfolding of a game to the audience. I feel that a major league broadcaster should have minor league experiences broadcasting before making it to the "big show." You will probably learn more about the game of baseball in the minor leagues than jumping right into the broadcast booth at the major league level. I spent ten years broadcasting minor league baseball before making it to the "big league" level on a full-time basis, and I will never forgot the experiences that prepped me to become a major league broadcaster.

Just because you can't make it as a player doesn't mean you can't make to the "big leagues" in another capacity. I didn't give up, and neither should you.

"Touch 'em All,"

—John Gordon
Play-by-Play Broadcaster, Minnesota Twins Radio Network